TABLE OF CONTENTS

The glorious Aesir (AY-zir) were the gods of the ancient Norse people. Viking tribes believed their gods lived in the heavenly realm of Asgard and ruled over the world of mortals and the lands of the dead. The Vikings believed in numerous gods and told many stories about them. The most dramatic story of all is the tale of how the gods meet their end.

Odin, ruler of the gods, prized wisdom above all things. Through his pursuit of knowledge, he learned about a terrible prophesy concerning the final fate of the Aesir. One day, the Norse gods and their ancient enemies, the giants of Jötunheim, would fight in a final, glorious battle: Ragnarök – the Twilight of the Gods.

The gods of Asgard would emerge victorious if they faced only their giant enemies. But during this final conflict they face other foes too horrible to imagine. Fierce, bloodthirsty monsters. An army of the dead. The savage Surtur and his legions of fiery warriors. All are eager to seek the end of the Aesir.

The Norse gods fight valiantly and destroy many of their most powerful enemies. But in spite of their bravery, most of the Aesir meet their final fate. And in the end, the world is consumed by the rage of Surtur's fire.

For a time only darkness rules across the land. But, like the Norse gods themselves, the darkness eventually comes to an end. As Odin has also foreseen, one day the light will shine again upon a renewed and hopeful world...

NORSE MYTHS

A VIKING GRAPHIC NOVEL

TWILIGHT OF THE GODS

by MICHAEL DAHL and EDUARDO GARCIA

Raintree is an imprint of Capstone Global Library
Limited, a company incorporated in England and
Wales having its registered office at 264 Banbury
Road, Oxford, OX2 7DY – Registered company
number: 6695582

www.raintree.co.uk
myorders@raintree.co.uk

Text © Capstone Global Library Limited 2017
The moral rights of the proprietor have been
asserted.

Edited by Aaron Sautter
Designed by Kristi Carlson
Production by Laura Manthe
Printed and bound in China

ISBN 978 1 4747 2521 7
20 19 18 17 16
10 9 8 7 6 5 4 3 2 1

British Library Cataloguing in Publication Data
A full catalogue record for this book is available
from the British Library.

Odin – the one-eyed All-Father and ruler of the Norse gods. He knows that Ragnarök means the end of the world – and that none will escape their fate.

 Thor – the fearless, red-headed god of thunder. Thor uses his magical warhammer, Mjölnir (MYOHL-neer), to smite Asgard's enemies.

 Heimdall (HAYM-doll) – the watchman of the gods. Heimdall sounds his horn, Gjallarhorn (YAHL-ahr-hawrn), to call the Aesir to the final battle.

 Vidar the Silent – a quiet and peaceful god. But when Odin falls in battle, Vidar fiercely avenges his father. He then becomes the leader of the new gods when the world is restored.

 Loki – a small giant and blood brother to the gods. His anger towards Baldur leads to actions that trigger Ragnarök. Loki leads an army of giants and monsters into battle against the Aesir.

 Angrboda – one of Loki's two wives. Angrboda hears Loki's call and sends her monstrous children to battle the gods.

 Surtur – ruler of the fiery land of Muspelheim (MOO-spell-haym). At Ragnarök he battles the god Frey and brings fire to consume the world.

  Fenrir and Garm – a giant wolf and a monstrous hound that bring terror and grief to the Aesir during Ragnarök.

 Jörmungandr (YOOR-muhn-guhn-dar) – a colossal snake, also known as the Midgard Serpent. Thor and the monster meet their fate together during the final battle.

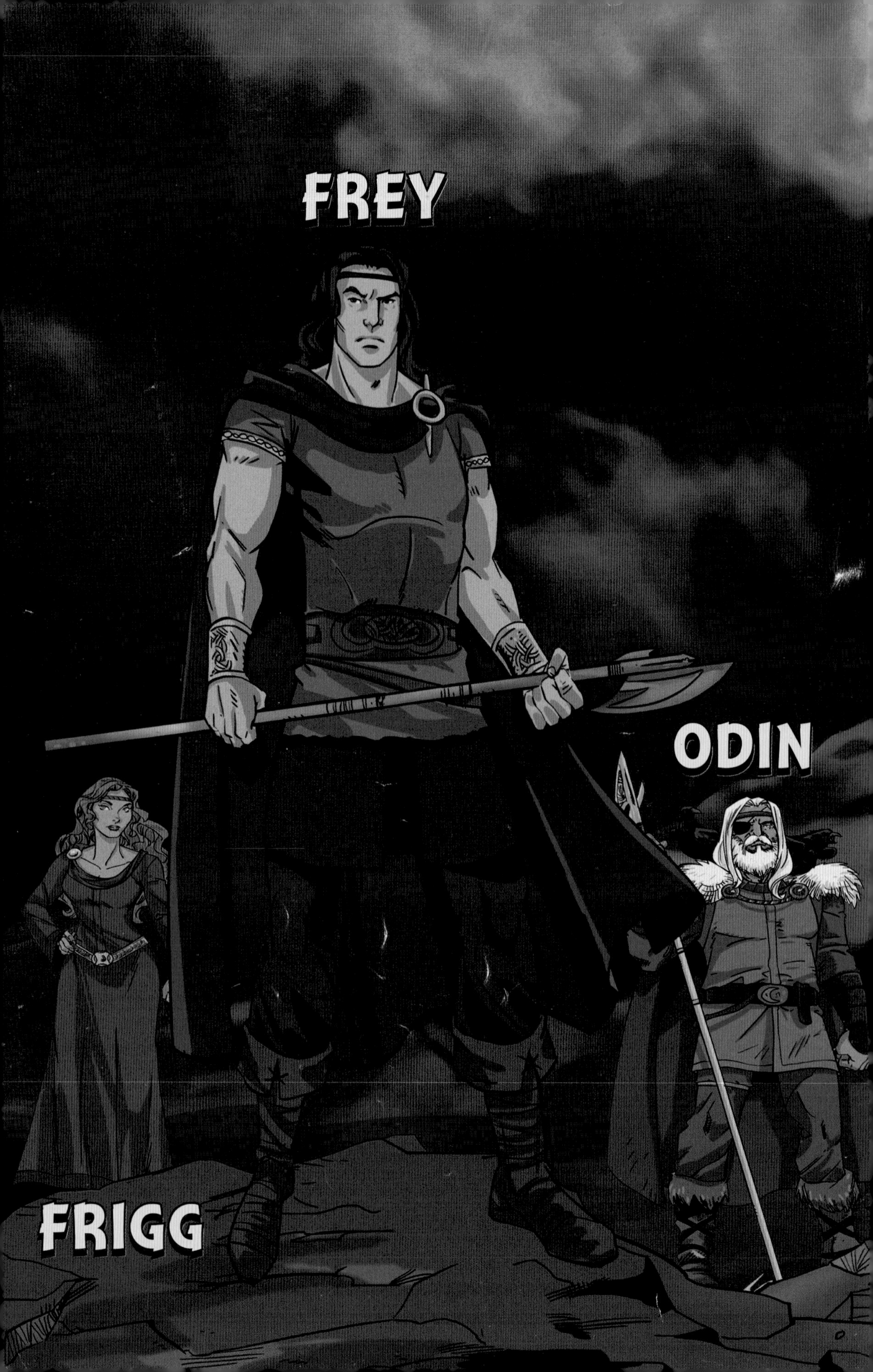
FREY
ODIN
FRIGG

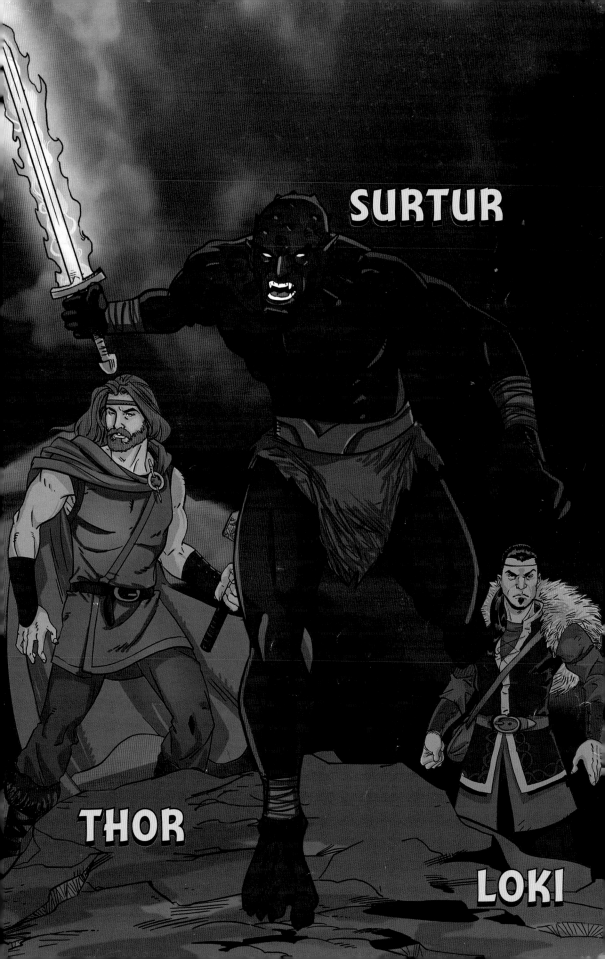

The gods of Asgard and the giants have long been at war with each other.

Odin, father of the gods, wanted peace with the giants. So he took in Loki, a young giant, and raised him among the other gods.

But Loki later betrayed the gods of Asgard.

Loki was jealous of Baldur, Odin's favoured son.

He created a dart of mistletoe and killed his adoptive brother.

In so doing, Loki set in motion the events that would lead to the end of the world…

TWILIGHT OF THE GODS

CHAPTER 1
THE BREAKING OF CHAINS

For his crime, Loki was imprisoned and punished…

None felt pity for Loki. He was a giant, after all, and they were gods from Asgard.

And Odin's decisions were final.

But after the gods left the scene...

The vicious wolves are Sköll, which is Treachery ...

... terrible cold and darkness covered the world.

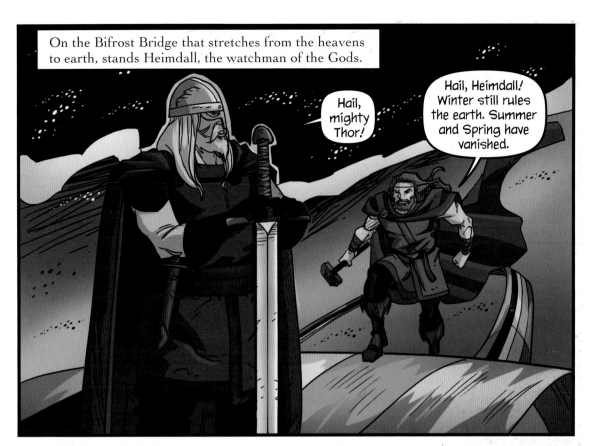

On the Bifrost Bridge that stretches from the heavens to earth, stands Heimdall, the watchman of the Gods.

Hail, mighty Thor!

Hail, Heimdall! Winter still rules the earth. Summer and Spring have vanished.

Why do you frown, ever-watchful Heimdall?

I hear the sound of *death*, Thor.

Meanwhile, back in Asgard, the realm of the gods…

I now hear the breaking of chains! *Loki is free!*

The shuddering of Yggdrasil has loosened Loki's bonds.

Freedom!

CLINK

CLINK

Husband, please don't go! You are heading to your *doom!*

Bah! I make my *own* fate.

CHAPTER 2:
THE GATHERING ARMIES

The Gods of Asgard gather at Heimdall's call.

The monstrous serpent, the spawn of Loki, whips the waves of the ocean. The growing flood reaches the gates of Jötunheim, home of the giants.

Naglfar — a vessel made of dead men's fingernails. The ship was built by the giants through untold ages, waiting for this fated day.

The evil ship plunges toward the land of mortals.

Loki pilots the ship, leading the giants against the gods of Asgard.

Odin calls out to the god of strength and sunlight.

CHAPTER 3
THE WAR OF THE GODS

The Plain of Vidgard ... the final battleground.

A third army arrives to join the battle.

Hel, Queen of the Underworld and ally to the giants, leads an army of the dead against the gods.

The great dog Garm hungers for blood…

GRRRRR!

The forces prepare for battle, three armies against one. The Giants, the dead, and the legions of fire — all against the Gods of Asgard!

As the armies face each other, another prophecy comes true. The last battle is announced by the screams of Hresvelgr, the Swallower of Corpses.

Meanwhile, Odin fends off the attacks of the ferocious Fenrir…

I don't care that Ragnarök is here. If I am to die, I'll take you with me, *foul beast!*

CHAPTER 4
THE LAST STAND OF THE AESIR

On the other side of the world, in the Forest of Memory…

Vidar, the Silent … the Solitary … has long mourned his fallen brother, Baldur.

ASGARD!

Vidar hears his father's dying cry on the wind.

My father!

But the serpent's poisonous breath is its final — and most powerful — weapon.

COUGH! HACK!

No enemy blade or spear could fell the mighty Thor. Only the poisonous breath of evil.

Surtur smiles with victory. His burning sword glows brighter ...

... the Twilight of the Gods is at hand.

Ragnarök — the end of the world — has come.

CHAPTER 5
A NEW WORLD

The flames consumed all, leaving behind only darkness. Complete emptiness touched every corner of the world …

… except for one.

Gimli, the Glittering Hall. The tallest palace of Asgard …

ABOUT THE RETELLING
AUTHOR AND ILLUSTRATOR

Michael Dahl is the prolific author of the critically acclaimed Troll Hunters adventure series and more than 200 other books for children and young adults. He has won the AEP Distinguished Achievement Award three times for his non-fiction and has been shortlisted twice by the Agatha Awards for his mysteries for young readers.

In addition to his writing, Dahl is also a popular speaker at numerous schools, libraries and conferences, including the American Library Association, the American Association of School Librarians, the Texas Library Association and the International Reading Association.

Dahl currently lives in Minneapolis, Minnesota,USA, a northern realm favourable to both trolls and Norse gods.

Passionate comic book artist **Eduardo Garcia** works from his studio (Red Wolf Studio) in Mexico City with the help of his talented son, Sebastian Iñaki. He has brought his talent, pencils and colours to varied projects for many titles and publishers such as Scooby-Doo (DC Comics), Spiderman Family (Marvel), Flash Gordon (Aberdeen) and Speed Racer (IDW).

GLOSSARY

Aesir the name given to the collection of gods and goddesses found in the ancient Norse religion

avenge to harm or punish someone who has harmed you or someone or something that you care about

exiled ordered or forced to leave one's own country

fate the supernatural force that some people believe controls events and decides what happens

Jötunheim the land of the giants in ancient Norse mythology

mistletoe a plant with thick leaves and white berries that grows on some trees

mortal unable to live forever

prophecy a prediction

venom poisonous liquid produced by some animals

Yggdrasil a huge ash tree in Norse mythology that spreads across the universe; it binds together heaven, hell and the worlds of the living and the dead

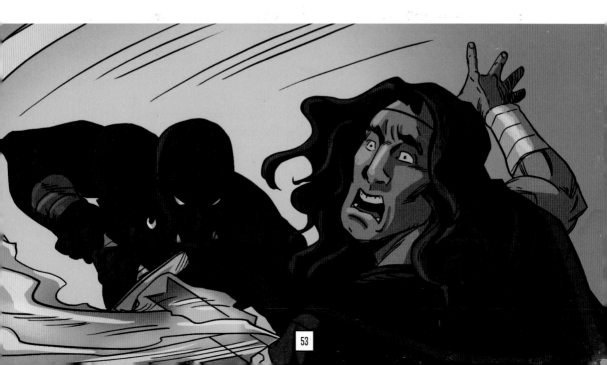

DISCUSSION QUESTIONS

1. Odin knew that when Ragnarök came, it would be the end of the
    Aesir's rule. Do you think Odin should have warned the other gods
    or could have done anything to stop the end of the world?

2. When Loki is freed from his chains, he chooses to lead an army of
    giants against the gods. Why do you think he chose to go to war
    instead of seeking peace?

3. When Vidar hears his father's dying cry, he is alone in a distant
    forest. Why do you think he was not with the rest of the gods at
    the final battle?

WRITING PROMPTS

1. At the beginning of the story, Loki is sentenced to suffer forever for killing Baldur. Do you think it was a fair punishment? Write down the punishment you would give Loki for his crimes.

2. The fiery giant Surtur claims that the Norse gods forced him into exile. Write a short story describing what Surtur might have done that resulted in his exile.

3. At the end of the story, the world is renewed, and Vidar becomes the leader of the new gods. Write your own story about the new world, the people who live in it and how Vidar becomes a wise ruler.

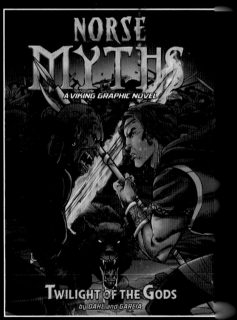